IGOR STRAVINSKY

DUMBARTON OAKS

Concerto in E flat
for Chamber Orchestra

Ernst Eulenburg Ltd

London · Mainz · Madrid · New York · Paris · Prague · Tokyo · Toronto · Zürich

CONTENTS

PREFACE

On 18 December 1936 Stravinsky set out on a tour of the United States to go, after concerts in Toronto and New York, to Hollywood, where he again met Charlie Chaplin, among others. At the end of the tour he conducted the rehearsals and the premiere of his ballet *Jeu de Cartes* in the Metropolitan Opera, New York. He began his return journey to Europe on 5 May 1937 and arrived back in Paris on 11 May. During his American visit Stravinsky also stayed in Washington, where he became acquainted with Mrs R. W. Bliss and admired her villa, with its splendid park, in Dumbarton Oaks. This patroness of the arts, whose house was the focal point of many artistic events, first commissioned him to compose a 'concerto' for her 30th wedding anniversary in 1938, then, a little later, the *Symphony in C* to celebrate the 50th concert season (1940/41) of the Chicago Symphony Orchestra.

Stravinsky spent the summer of 1937 at the Château de Monthoux near Annemasse in Savoy. There the first movement was written of the *Dumbarton Oaks Concerto in E flat*, which, as Stravinsky informed Willy Strecker,[1] had already been begun on 23 July. Stravinsky wrote to Samuel Dushkin on 8 August that, had it not been for the uncertainty and anxiety over his wife's illness, the summer would have passed very well for him.

Preliminary discussions on the commissioned composition for Mrs Bliss had taken place in the USA, but a definite agreement was reached only through the intervention of Nadia Boulanger. She telegraphed to Washington: 'Stravinsky desires to know should begin composition for you suggest 2500 dollars accepts compose music Brandenburg Concerto dimensions.'[2] According to the letter of 24 October

to Dushkin, the first movement was complete and already orchestrated. Meantime the downpayment on the commission was also made. The composer wrote to Willy Strecker on 3 January 1938: 'The composition of the second movement, which is called Intermezzo and is an allegretto, is finished.'[3] The succeeding stages of the completion of *Dumbarton Oaks* can be elicited from the further exchanges of letters with his friend Strecker, as follows:

Concerto in E flat: the proofs likewise received. Have not yet started correcting them, being in a hurry to finish the instrumentation of the second movement, the two-piano transcription of which is just completed. (20.1.38)

I have just sent you by registered mail the second movement of my Concerto – manuscript of the orchestral score and the two-piano reduction. (24.1.38)

I have just received from Mainz two copies of the proofs of the second movement of my Concerto, but without my manuscript. (17.2.38)

The third part of my Concerto is proceeding well. But it is difficult for me to tell you exactly the date by which I reckon to finish it. In three weeks, roughly. You should know that my work was constantly interrupted by concert tours. Fortunately the month of March is mine; there is only the radio concert this 4th of March (*Jeu de Cartes* and *Symphonie de Psaumes* at the Salle Gaveau), after which I can devote myself entirely to my Concerto, to finishing the third movement and to the proofs. (27.2.38)

The completion of my score is a little behind time, I know, but you would well understand if I told you of the state of continual anxiety in which I live, with these distressing worries about my wife and about Mika [Stravinsky's daughter]. (20.3.38)

In a few days I will send you the last pages of the orchestral score of the Concerto, the music of which I

---

[1] Willy and Ludwig Strecker at that time were directors of B. Schott's Söhne, Mainz.
[2] *Stravinsky in Pictures and Documents* (New York 1978), 339

[3] All letters quoted are to be found in the archives of B. Schott's Söhne. Original French wording cf. VIII.

have finished. I am very happy that this Concerto pleases you […] (29.3.38)

The composer's last years in Paris were clouded by numerous tribulations. During this time occured the deaths of his eldest daughter (1938), his wife and his mother (both 1939). An increasing opposition to his music was becoming manifest among the musical public. His latest work, *Jeu de Cartes*, after its New York premiere was indeed given in Dresden but not in Paris, since Stravinsky could not get his way in his wish for a choreographer acceptable to him. Also the performance of *Dumbarton Oaks* was clearly more successful in Washington than in Paris, where it was given in the Salle Gaveau under Stravinsky's direction a month after the world premiere. In the *Journal de Paris* of 13 October 1938 appeared an interview with Stravinsky in which he complained that he had not been given adequate opportunities to exercise his capabilities as a composer and his activities as a conductor. As a further cause of his dissatisfaction with France, a fruitless candidature for the Institut de France can be mentioned: at the election of a new member the less distinguished Florent Schmitt was preferred to him. The negative publicity associated with this, after an article by Guermantes in *Le Figaro* entitled *Le Sacre de l'automne*, made it appreciably easier for Stravinsky to decide to emigrate to the USA. Besides the lively interest in performances of his works and the commissions for compositions, Stravinsky felt honoured and attracted by the invitation from Edward W. Forbes, chairman of Harvard University's Charles Eliot Norton Professorship Committee, to hold the chair of poetry at Harvard for a fee of 10,000 dollars.

The bitter last months in Europe, during which he still composed the first movement of the *Symphony in C* in the Rue St Honoré in Paris, were also darkened by political events (the Munich Agreement of 1939) and the condemnation of his compositions in the Düsseldorf exhibition of 'degenerate art' in May 1938. The French ambassador in Berlin at that time, François Poncet, lodged a protest against the discrimination against the French citizen Stravinsky. This led to a response by the German Foreign Ministry in which it stated that the criticism was directed not against Stravinsky personally but against the tendencies in the new music represented by him and by Hindemith.

Stravinsky's health was so impaired at the beginning of 1938 that he could not conduct the premiere of *Dumbarton Oaks* in Washington himself. He entrusted the task to Nadia Boulanger, under whose baton the work was first performed on 8 May. Mrs Bliss telegraphed to Paris: 'Performance Concerto Dumbarton Oaks worthy of the work'. According to Dushkin, who was present at the performance, it was 'a great success'. The *Concerto in E flat* received the name *Dumbarton Oaks* at the wish of Mrs Bliss, who commissioned it and who preferred this title for the concerto to a personal dedication.

The first edition of the score, which appeared from Schott's in July 1938, is dated '8.V.38' (the day of the world premiere). The complete autograph is in the possession of Harvard University but is housed in Dumbarton Oaks in Washington, DC. In addition, in Stravinsky's estate two pages of undated autograph sketches for this work are preserved in an envelope. The four-hand piano score was prepared by the composer himself.

It is in accord with Stravinsky's aesthetic views that nothing of his depressing personal situation at the time of composing the *Concerto in E flat* entered into the work itself. He emphatically rejected any biographical or emotional reference in a work to the composer's life. It is therefore not surprising that the effect of the *Concerto in E flat*, by its classical transparence, is confident and cheerful. Today it seems barely comprehensible that this work, with which Stravinsky ceased writing on the Baroque model (apart from later reminiscences), aroused so much hostility and criticism. The opponents of Stravinsky's neo-classicism were called to the colours once again. René Leibowitz, for example, deplored Stravinsky's 'insolent borrowing of a theme from Bach' (*Esprit*,

1 July 1938). This criticism was a continuation of the long sustained disparagement of the composer in the press, for instance by Maurice Delage and Constant Lambert, but also by Arnold Schoenberg.

Stravinsky's involvement with concerto form did not first begin with *Dumbarton Oaks*. He had tried out this form since the Piano Concerto of 1923/24, the *Capriccio* of 1929, the Violin Concerto of 1931, the *Concerto for two pianos* of 1935, and after *Dumbarton Oaks* put forward further works of this type with the *Danses Concertantes*, the *Ebony Concerto* and the *Concerto in D for strings*. With *Dumbarton Oaks* also originated Stravinsky's intention of writing a symphony for large orchestra. The commission for the *Symphony in C* thus came at exactly the right moment. In contrast to the *Concerto in E flat*, Stravinsky no longer orientated himself on Bach, but on the classical Haydn and Beethoven. The *Symphony in C* is framed by the chamber orchestral works *Dumbarton Oaks* and the *Danses Concertantes* just as is the *Symphony in three movements*, from the years 1943/44, between the *Ebony Concerto* and the *Concerto in D for strings*. The general impression of the first movement of *Dumbarton Oaks* is akin to that of the first movement of the *Sonata for two pianos* of 1943/44 and of the Septet of 1952/53. According to Alfredo Casella, the theme of the second movement bears a great similarity to 'Se Falstaff s'assotiglia' from Act 1 of Verdi's *Falstaff*.

Herbert Schneider
Translation: Lionel Salter

VORWORT

Stravinsky trat am 18. Dezember 1936 eine Reise in die Vereinigten Staaten an, um sich nach Konzerten in Toronto und New York nach Hollywood zu begeben, wo er u. a. Charlie Chaplin wiederbegegnete. Zuletzt leitete er die Proben und die Uraufführung seines Balletts *Jeu de Cartes* in der Metropolitan Opera in New York. Am 5. Mai 1937 trat er die Rückreise nach Europa an und kam am 11. Mai wieder in Paris an. Während seines Amerikabesuchs weilte Stravinsky auch in Washington, lernte dort Mrs. R. W. Bliss kennen und bewunderte ihre Villa mit einem großartigen Park in Dumbarton Oaks. Diese Kunstmäzenin, deren Haus Mittelpunkt vieler künstlerischer Ereignisse war, gab ihm zunächst den Auftrag, für ihren 30. Hochzeitstag im Jahre 1938 ein „Concerto", dann kurze Zeit später die *Symphony in C* für die Feier der 50. Konzertsaison des Chicago Symphony Orchestra 1940/41 zu komponieren.

Den Sommer des Jahres 1937 verbrachte Stravinsky auf Château de Monthoux in Annemasse in Savoyen. Dort entstand der erste Satz von *Dumbarton Oaks Concerto en Mi b*, der, wie Stravinsky Willy Strecker[1] mitteilte, am 23. Juli bereits begonnen war. An Samuel Dushkin schrieb Stravinsky am 8. August, hätten ihn nicht die Ungewissheit und die Sorgen über die Krankheit seiner Frau belastet, wäre der Sommer für ihn sehr gut verlaufen.

Die Vorgespräche für die Auftragskomposition für Mrs. Bliss hatten in den USA stattgefunden, aber erst durch Vermittlung von Nadia Boulanger kam die endgültige Vereinbarung zustande. Sie telegrafierte nach Washington: „Stravinsky möchte wissen will Komposition für Sie beginnen schlägt 2500 Dollar vor stimmt der Komposition eines Werkes in den Dimensionen der Brandenburgischen Konzerte zu."[2]

Dem Brief an Dushkin vom 24. Oktober zufolge war der erste Satz fertig und bereits orchestriert. Die Anzahlung der Auftraggeberin war auch inzwischen erfolgt. An Willy Strecker schrieb der Komponist am 3. Januar 1938: „Die Komposition des zweiten Teils, der Intermezzo heißt und ein Allegretto ist, ist beendet."[3] Aus dem weiteren Briefwechsel mit seinem Freund Strecker sind die weiteren Situationen der Fertigstellung von *Dumbarton Oaks* folgendermaßen zu eruieren:

Concerto in Es: die Korrekturfahnen ebenfalls erhalten. Korrektur noch nicht begonnen, da ich die Instrumentierung des zweiten Satzes, dessen Transkription für zwei Klaviere gerade beendet ist, rasch fertigstellen will. (20. 1. 1938)

Ich habe Ihnen per Einschreiben den 2. Satz meines Concerto in Partitur und in vierhändigem Klavierauszug zugeschickt. (24. 1. 1938)

Ich habe aus Mainz die Korrekturfahnen des 2. Satzes meines Concerto in zwei Exemplaren erhalten, aber nicht das Manuskript. (17. 2. 1938)

Der 3. Teil meines Concerto geht gut voran. Es ist aber schwer, Ihnen genau das Datum zu nennen, wann ich ihn fertigstellen werde. Ungefähr in drei Wochen. Man muß wissen, daß meine Arbeit ständig durch Konzertreisen unterbrochen wird. Glücklicherweise gehört mir der Monat März ganz, es gibt nur noch das Radio-Konzert am 4. März (*Jeu de Cartes* und *Symphonie de Psaumes* in der Salle Gaveau), nach diesem werde ich mich ganz dem Concerto widmen, der Beendigung des 3. Teils und der Korrekturen. (27. 2. 1938)

Der Abschluß meiner Partitur hat sich ein wenig verzögert, aber Sie werden es gut verstehen, wenn ich Ihnen von meinem Zustand ständiger Ungewißheit berichte, in dem ich wegen der quälenden Sorgen um meine Frau und Mika [Tochter Stravinskys] lebe. (20. 3. 1938)

---

[1] Willy und Ludwig Strecker leiteten zu dieser Zeit den Verlag B. Schott's Söhne, Mainz.

[2] *Stravinsky in Pictures and Documents*, New York 1978, S. 339.

[3] Verlags B. Schott's Söhne in Mainz, Französischer Originaltext s. S. VIII.

In einigen Tagen sende ich Ihnen die letzten Seiten der Orchesterpartitur des Concerto, dessen Komposition ich beendet habe. Ich bin sehr glücklich, daß Ihnen das Concerto gefällt […]. (29. 3. 1938)

Die letzten Jahre des Komponisten in Paris waren von zahlreichen Sorgen getrübt. In diese Zeit fallen der Tod seiner ältesten Tochter (1938), der seiner Frau und seiner Mutter (beide 1939). In der musikalischen Öffentlichkeit machte sich eine zunehmende Opposition gegen seine Musik bemerkbar. Sein neuestes Werk, *Jeu de Cartes*, wurde nach der New Yorker Uraufführung zwar in Dresden, nicht aber in Paris gegeben, da Stravinsky sich mit seinem Wunsch nach einem ihm geeigneten Choreographen nicht durchsetzen konnte. Auch die Aufführung von *Dumbarton Oaks* war offensichtlich in Washington erfolgreicher als in Paris, wo sie in der Salle Gaveau einen Monat nach der Uraufführung unter der Leitung Stravinskys stattfand. Im *Journal de Paris* vom 13. Oktober 1938 erschien ein Interview mit Stravinsky, in dem er sich beklagte, dass ihm in Paris keine ausreichenden Gelegenheiten gegeben würden, seine kompositorischen Fähigkeiten und seine Dirigiertätigkeit auszuüben. Als weiterer Grund für seine Unzufriedenheit mit Frankreich ist eine vergebliche Kandidatur für das Institut de France zu nennen. Bei der Wahl eines neuen Mitglieds wurde ihm der weniger bedeutende Florent Schmitt vorgezogen. Die damit zusammenhängende negative Publizität nach einem *Le Sacre de l'automne* betitelten Aufsatz von Guermantes im *Figaro* hat Stravinsky die Entscheidung, nach den USA überzusiedeln, wesentlich erleichtert. Neben dem lebhaften Interesse an Aufführungen seiner Werke und den Kompositionsaufträgen empfand Stravinsky die Einladung von Edward W. Forbes, dem Chairman des Harvard University's Charles Eliot Norton Professorship Committees, gegen ein Honorar von 10.000 Dollar den Lehrstuhl für Poetik der Harvard University zu vertreten, als außerordentlich ehrenvoll und verlockend.

Die bitteren letzten Monate in Europa, während derer er in der Rue Saint Honoré in Paris noch den ersten Satz der *Symphony in C*

komponierte, waren auch durch die politischen Ereignisse (Münchner Abkommen 1939) und die Verurteilung seiner Kompositionen während der Düsseldorfer Ausstellung „Entartete Musik" im Mai 1938 verdüstert. Der damalige französische Botschafter in Berlin, François Poncet, trug einen Protest gegen die Diskriminierung des französischen Staatsbürgers Stravinsky vor. Dies führte zu einer Reaktion des deutschen Außenministeriums, in dem es heißt, die Kritik richte sich nicht gegen Stravinsky persönlich, sondern gegen Tendenzen in der Neuen Musik, die von ihm und Hindemith vertreten würden.

Stravinskys Gesundheit war zu Beginn des Jahres 1938 so angegriffen, dass er die Uraufführung von *Dumbarton Oaks* in Washington nicht selbst leiten konnte. Er übertrug die Aufgabe Nadia Boulanger, unter deren Stabführung das Werk am 8. Mai uraufgeführt wurde. Mrs. Bliss telegrafierte nach Paris: „Aufführung, die der Komposition würdig war". Nach Dushkin, der an der Aufführung mitwirkte, war es ein „großer Erfolg". Den Namen *Dumbarton Oaks* erhielt das *Concerto in Es* auf Wunsch der Auftraggeberin, Mrs. Bliss, die diese Betitelung des Konzerts einer persönlichen Widmung vorzog.

Der Erstdruck der Partitur, die bei Schott im Juli 1938 erschien, ist „8.V.38" (Tag der Uraufführung) datiert. Das vollständige Autograph ist im Besitz der Harvard University, befindet sich aber in Dumbarton Oaks in Washington. In Stravinskys Nachlass sind außerdem in einem Umschlag zwei Seiten nicht datierter autographer Skizzen zu diesem Werk erhalten. Den vierhändigen Klavierauszug fertigte der Komponist selbst an.

Es entspricht den ästhetischen Auffassungen Stravinskys, dass von seiner bedrückenden persönlichen Situation der Entstehungszeit des *Concerto in Es* nichts in das Werk selbst eingegangen ist. Einen biographisch-emotionalen Bezug der Komposition zum Leben des Komponisten lehnte er entschieden ab. Es verwundert daher nicht, dass die Wirkung des *Concerto in Es* durch seine klassische Transparenz eher zuversichtlich und heiter ist. Heute erscheint es kaum noch verständlich, dass dieses Werk, mit dem Stravinsky, abgesehen von späteren Reminiszenzen, die Komposition nach Barockmodellen abschloss, so viel Feindschaft und Kritik hervorrief. Die Gegner des Neoklassizismus Stravinskys waren erneut auf den Plan gerufen. René Leibowitz z. B. beklagte Stravinskys „unverschämtes Entlehnen eines Themas von Bach" (*Esprit*, 1. Juli 1938). Diese Kritik war eine Fortsetzung der seit längerem anhaltenden Herabsetzung des Komponisten in der Presse, etwa bei Maurice Delage und Constant Lambert, aber auch durch Arnold Schönberg.

Stravinskys Auseinandersetzung mit der Konzertform begann nicht erst mit *Dumbarton Oaks*. Seit dem Klavierkonzert von 1923/24, dem *Capriccio* von 1929, dem Violinkonzert von 1931, dem *Konzert für zwei Klaviere* von 1935 hatte er diese Form erprobt und nach *Dumbarton Oaks* mit den *Danses Concertantes*, dem *Ebony Concerto* und dem *Concerto in D für Streicher* weitere Werke dieses Typs vorgelegt. Mit *Dumbarton Oaks* entstand auch Stravinskys Intention, eine Symphonie für großes Orchester zu schreiben. Der Kompositionsauftrag für die *Symphony in C* kam somit gerade im rechten Augenblick. Im Gegensatz zum *Concerto in Es* orientierte sich Stravinsky nicht mehr an Bach, sondern an den Klassikern Haydn und Beethoven. Die *Symphony in C* ist mit *Dumbarton Oaks* und den *Danses Concertantes* ebenso von Kammerorchesterwerken eingerahmt wie die *Symphonie in drei Sätzen* aus den Jahren 1943/44 durch das *Ebony Concerto* und das *Concerto in D für Streicher*. Dem Gesamteindruck des ersten Satzes von *Dumbarton Oaks* ist der erste Satz der Sonate für zwei Klaviere aus den Jahren 1943/44 und das Septett von 1952/53 verwandt. Das Thema des zweiten Satzes hat Alfredo Casella zufolge große Ähnlichkeit mit „Se Falstaff s'assotiglia" aus dem ersten Akt von Guiseppe Verdis *Falstaff*.

Herbert Schneider

Original French Quotations/
Originaltext der französischen Zitate

'La composition de la deuxième partie qui s'appelle Intermezzo et qui est un allegretto est terminée.'
'CONCERTO in Mi bémol: les épreuves également reçu. Pas encore commencé de les corriger étant pressé de finir l'instrumentation du second mouvement dont la transcription pour deux pianos vient d'être achevée.' (20. 1. 1938)
'Je viens vous expédier sous pli recommandé le deuxième mouvement de mon CONCERTO-manuscrit de la part. d'orchestre et la réduction pour deux pianos.' (24. 1. 1938)
'Je viens de recevoir de Mayence les épreuves du second mouvement de mon CONCERTO en deux exemplaires mais sans mon manuscrit.' (17. 2. 1938)
'La troisième partie de mon CONCERTO avance. Il m'est cependant difficile à vous dire exactement la date à laquelle je compte de la terminer. Dans trois semaines à peu près. Il faut savoir que mon travail était constamment interrompu par des voyages de concerts. Heureusement le mois de mars est à moi, il y a seulement le concert de la radio, ce 4 mars (Jeu de Cartes et Symphonie de Psaumes à la salle Gaveau) après quoi je m'adonne entièrement à mon CONCERTO, à l'achèvement de sa troisième partie et aux épreuves.' (27. 2. 1938)
'L'achèvement de ma partition est un peu en retard, le je sais, mais vous me comprendrai bien si je vous racontais de mon état de continuelle inquiétude dans lequel je vis avec ces pénibles soucis tantôt pour ma femme tantôt pour Mika.' (20. 3. 1938)
'Dans quelques jours je vous enverrai les dernières pages de la part. d'orchestre du CONCERTO dont je viens de terminer la musique. Je suis très heureux que ce CONCERTO vous plaise […].' (29. 3. 1938)

Facsimiles on following pages

Facsimile I
Concerto en mi♭ pour petit orchestre
Igor Strawinsky
First sketches

Noted at the top of the page are the theme of the first movement in B major and several motifs which Stravinsky only partly used. In the middle, after figure 3, the outline of the theme and its harmonization as it finally appears in bb12–18 is already recognizable; accentuation and articulation marks are still missing. The continuation corresponds to b5 of figure 5 and the last bar of figure 6. Underneath, the composer has already written the violin part for two bars before figure 4.

Facsimile II
Igor Strawinsky
Concerto en mi♭
Definitive sketches

The preliminary orchestral sketch of the beginning of *Dumbarton Oaks* showing all structural, thematic and contrapuntal details as well as the most important points of instrumentation. This page corresponds to the final score up to figure 4 (bb1–22).

Facsimile III
First page of the autograph full score

Zu den folgenden Faksimiles

Faksimile I
Concerto en mi♭ pour petit orchestre
Igor Strawinsky
Erste Skizzen

Auf der Seite sind oben zunächst das Thema des ersten Satzes in B-Dur sowie verschiedene Motive notiert, die Strawinsky nur teilweise verwendet hat. In der Mitte nach „3" erkennt man bereits die Gestalt des Themas und seiner Harmonisierung, wie es endgültig in T. 12–18 erscheint. Hier fehlen noch die Artikulations- und Betonungszeichen. Die Fortsetzung entspricht T. 5 nach Ziffer 5 und der letzte Takt Ziffer 6. Darunter hat der Komponist bereits die Violinstimme zwei Takte vor Ziffer 4 der endgültigen Partitur aufgezeichnet.

Facsimile II
Igor Strawinsky
Concerto en mi♭
Particell

In diesem Particell des Anfangs von *Dumbarton Oaks* sind alle strukturellen thematischen und kontrapunktischen Details sowie die wichtigsten Angaben zur Instrumentation festgehalten. Diese Seite entspricht der endgültigen Partitur bis Ziffer 4 (T. 1–22).

Facsimile III
Autograph der ersten Partiturseite

Facsimile I
printed by permission of Dumbarton Oaks Research Library and Collection, Washington, DC

Facsimile II
printed by permission of Dumbarton Oaks Research Library and Collection, Washington, DC

Facsimile III
printed by permission of Dumbarton Oaks Research Library and Collection, Washington, DC

DUMBARTON OAKS

Concerto in E flat

Igor Stravinsky
(1882–1971)

Ernst Eulenburg Ltd, London/Mainz

No. 1813   EE 6775

3

4

5

5

14

III. Con moto ♩ = 160

Flauto grande

Clarinetto (B♭)

Fagotto

Corno (F)

3 Violini

3 Viole

2 Violoncelli

2 Contrabassi

28

43

Duration: 12 minutes